All to Build a Snowman

by Samuel Tang illustrated by Anja Rieger

 HOUGHTON MIFFLIN   BOSTON · MORRIS PLAINS, NJ

California · Colorado · Georgia · Illinois · New Jersey · Texas

Acknowledgments
All to Build a Snowman by Samuel Tang, illustrated by Anja Rieger.

Photography
23 Philip & Karen Smith/Tony Stone Images **24** Frank Simonetti/IndexStock **25** Ariel Skelley/The Stock Market **26** Lori Adamski Peek/Tony Stone Images **27** Dick Luria/FPG International **28** (l) Mark Hill/IndexStock **28** (tr) Peter Beck/The Stock Market **28** (br) VCG/FPG International **29** Ken Fisher/Tony Stone Images.

PRINTED IN THE U.S.A.

ISBN: 0-618-03646-6

3456789-B-06 05 04 03 02 01

Kim and Tim and their dog Slim
went out to build a snowman.

They pushed and packed,
and rolled and stacked,

all to build a snowman.

A lady sat near
and said, "Look here."

"What fun to build a snowman!"

Then wind and snow
startled a crow,

**making some branches
fall far below.**

That made some acorns
drop down and thump.

That made the kitten
meow and jump.

That made the dog
bark and chase.

That made Dad
get caught in the race.

That made the pigeons
flutter and fly.

That made the lady
begin to cry —

"Oh my!
Oh my!
Oh my!
Oh my!"

"My kitten is on
the snowman!"

The kitten, at last,
was safe and sound.

**Kim and Tim then
looked around,
amazed by everything
they found —**

all to build a snowman,

all to build a snowman!

What Can We Do?

What can we do on a sunny day?
We can build a sandcastle.

What can we do on a windy day?
We can fly a kite.

What can we do on a snowy day?
We can build a snowman.

What can we do on a rainy day?
We can play a game.

What is the weather like today?

What will you do?
How will you play?